The Magic School Bus

In the Time of the Dinosaurs

The Magic School Bus

In the Time of the Dinosaurs

By Joanna Cole
Illustrated by Bruce Degen

Scholastic Inc.
New York · Toronto · London · Auckland · Sydney
Mexico City · New Delhi · Hong Kong · Buenos Aires

The author and illustrator wish to thank Mark A. Norell,
Associate Curator of Vertebrate Paleontology, the American Museum of Natural History,
for his assistance in preparing this book.

For their helpful advice and consultation, thanks also to Armand Morgan,
Public Education Department, Yale-Peabody Museum of Natural History, New Haven,
Connecticut; Professor Leo J. Hickey, Curator of Paleobotany, Yale-Peabody Museum
of Natural History; and Dave Varricchio, expert of Tyrannosaurus Rex,
Museum of the Rockies, Bozeman, Montana.

ISBN-13: 978-0-590-44689-1
ISBN-10: 0-590-44689-4

44 43   12 13 14/0

Printed in the U.S.A.   08

The illustrator used pen and ink, watercolor, color pencil,
and gouache for the paintings in this book.

To Armand Morgan,
our personal guide to the time of the dinosaurs
J.C. & B.D.

It was Visitors Day at our school.
Parents, relatives, and friends
were coming that afternoon to see our work.
In Ms. Frizzle's class, we were making
the whole room into Dinosaur Land!

ROOM 101
Welcome to DINOSAUR LAND

CYCADS

Meet a Maiasaura on Visitors Day

Hello!

THIS WAY

Some Dinosaurs ate other Dinosaurs.
"Diner"-saur
UH-OH!
"Dinner"-saur

I LOVE VISITORS DAY!

MY PARENTS ARE COMING.

MY GRANDMA'S COMING. I HOPE SHE LIKES MY PROJECT.

ALL DINOSAURS LIVED IN PREHISTORIC TIMES by Shirley

OUR DINOSAUR BOOKS
We wrote them Ourselves.

SOME DINOSAURS WERE HUGE by Wanda

SOME DINOSAURS WERE SMALL by Keesha

SOME DINOSAURS WERE MEAT-EATERS by Tim

SOME DINOSAURS WERE PLANT-EATERS by Arnold

MODEL OF DINOSAUR SKELETON by Phoebe
Made from Chicken bones and clay

6

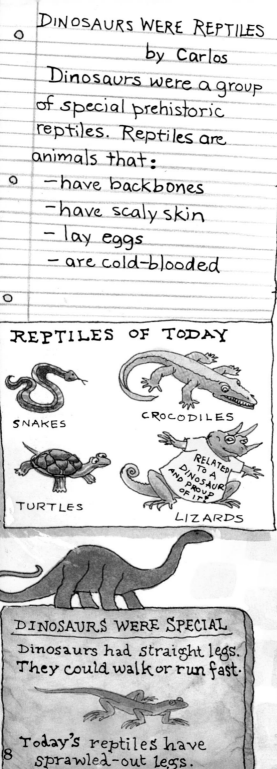

"Our class has been invited to a dinosaur dig," explained the Friz.
"We'll be leaving right away."
As we went out, one kid grabbed the video camera.
Others took along model dinosaurs for good luck.
When you have the wackiest teacher in school,
you need all the luck you can get!

WE'RE LEAVING NOW?

I GUESS MS. FRIZZLE FORGOT ABOUT VISITORS DAY.

SHE NEVER FORGOT ANYTHING BEFORE.

Dear Come and see the dinosaur bones we're digging up. Bring the whole class. Yours, Jeff

Ms. V. Frizzle SCHOOL U.S.A.

8

NO PEOPLE EVER SAW
A DINOSAUR   by Florrie
When early humans appeared on earth, dinosaurs had already been dead for millions of years!
People found out about dinosaurs from fossils.

FIVE KINDS OF DINOSAUR
FOSSILS   by Alex

1. BONES
2. TEETH
3. FOOTPRINTS
4. SKIN PRINTS
5. EGGS AND NESTS

As we rolled onto the highway,
Ms. Frizzle shouted from the driver's seat,
"We're on our way to fossil country, kids!
Who knows what a fossil is?"
Luckily, we had done our homework.
We knew a fossil is anything left
from a prehistoric animal or plant.

THIS STORY IS MAKE-BELIEVE.

THERE WERE NO DINOSAURS IN THE TIME OF CAVE PEOPLE.

After we had been driving for a long time, we came to a desert where people were working. Ms. Frizzle said this was the dinosaur dig. The people were paleontologists — scientists who study prehistoric life.

DINOSAURS LASTED FOR 150 MILLION YEARS ON EARTH! WEREN'T THEY AMAZING, ARNOLD?

IT'S AMAZING THAT I'VE LASTED THIS LONG IN MS. FRIZZLE'S CLASS.

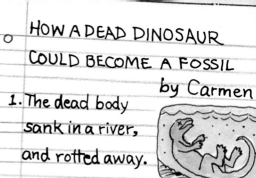

HOW A DEAD DINOSAUR COULD BECOME A FOSSIL
by Carmen

1. The dead body sank in a river, and rotted away.

2. The bones were covered with sand.

3. In time, the sand turned into rocks.

4. The bones became hard as rock, too.

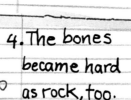

DID MOST DINOSAURS TURN INTO FOSSILS?

NO! DEAD DINOSAURS USUALLY ROTTED OR WERE EATEN.

DINOSAURS WERE SPECIAL
Dinosaurs were on earth 1500 times longer than humans have been so far.

We saw a gleam in Ms. Frizzle's eye.
"Want to look for some *Maiasaura* nests,
kids?" she shouted.
She rushed us onto the bus
and drove off.

We hadn't gone far when Ms. Frizzle
stopped the bus.
She turned a dial on the dashboard,
and the bus began to change.
It looked like a giant alarm clock.
Ms. Frizzle said it was a time machine!

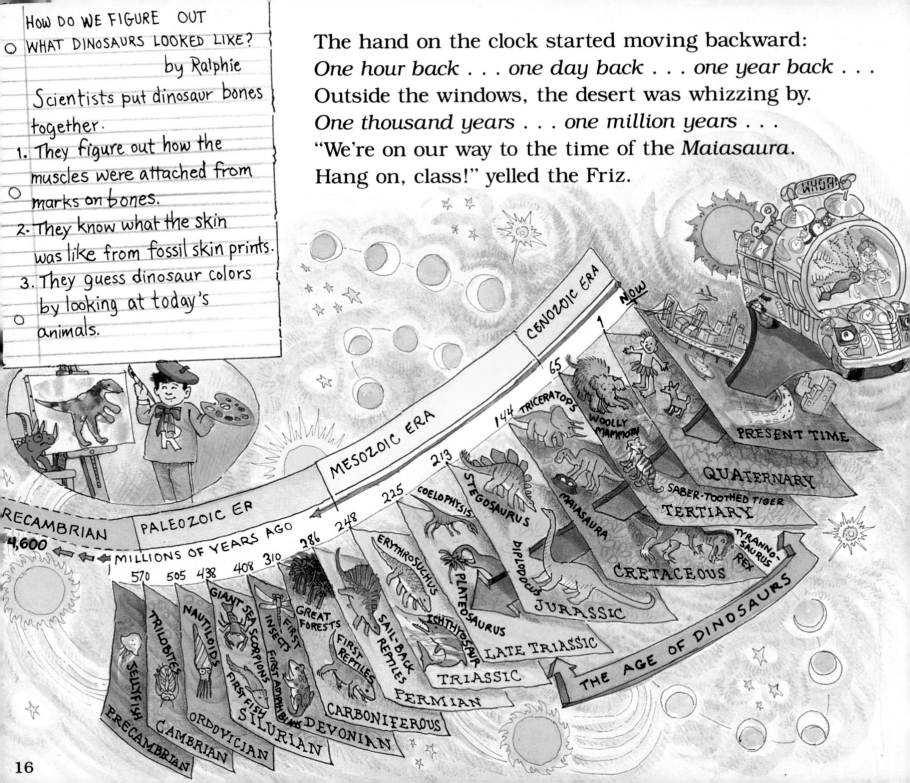

HOW DO WE FIGURE OUT
WHAT DINOSAURS LOOKED LIKE?
by Ralphie

Scientists put dinosaur bones together.
1. They figure out how the muscles were attached from marks on bones.
2. They know what the skin was like from fossil skin prints.
3. They guess dinosaur colors by looking at today's animals.

The hand on the clock started moving backward:
One hour back . . . one day back . . . one year back . . .
Outside the windows, the desert was whizzing by.
One thousand years . . . one million years . . .
"We're on our way to the time of the *Maiasaura.*
Hang on, class!" yelled the Friz.

WHOA!

CENOZOIC ERA

NOW

1

65

144 TRICERATOPS

WOOLLY MAMMOTH

PRESENT TIME

SABER-TOOTHED TIGER

QUATERNARY

MESOZOIC ERA

213

STEGOSAURUS

MAIASAURA

TERTIARY

225

COELOPHYSIS

DIPLODOCUS

TYRANNOSAURUS REX

CRETACEOUS

PALEOZOIC ER

248

ERYTHROSUCHUS

PLATEOSAURUS

JURASSIC

RECAMBRIAN

4,600

MILLIONS OF YEARS AGO

286

ICHTHYOSAUR

LATE TRIASSIC

THE AGE OF DINOSAURS

310

SAIL-BACK REPTILES

570 505 438 408

GREAT FORESTS

FIRST REPTILES

TRIASSIC

FIRST INSECTS

FIRST AMPHIBIANS

PERMIAN

TRILOBITES

NAUTILOIDS

GIANT SEA SCORPIONS

FIRST FISH

CARBONIFEROUS

JELLYFISH

ORDOVICIAN

SILURIAN

DEVONIAN

PRECAMBRIAN

CAMBRIAN

16

Suddenly, a large reptile rose out of the water and opened its huge mouth.
"That is not a dinosaur," Ms. Frizzle said.
"It's a phytosaur — a crocodile-like reptile."
The phytosaur caught a little dinosaur and pulled it underwater.
We wanted to get back on the bus, pronto!
But Ms. Frizzle said we had to learn about Triassic plant life.

AETOSAUR

PHYTOSAUR

ARE MEAT-EATERS MEAN?
by Arnold
No. Predators are part of nature. Hunting is the only way they can get their food.

SOME WORDS FROM DOROTHY ANN
A predator is a hunting animal.
Prey are the animals a predator hunts.

I'M A PREDATOR.

I'M PREY.

CONIFER

PLATEOSAUR

A sudden downpour caught us by surprise.
But the dinosaurs went right on eating.
We ran for the bus, and Frizzie called,
"Get ready to go *forward* in time, kids!"

IN A TROPICAL FOREST,
RAINS ARE FREQUENT
AND HEAVY, ARNOLD.

NOW SHE
TELLS ME!

JEFF WILL
LOVE THIS
VIDEO.

THE FIRST MAMMALS
LIVED WITH DINOSAURS
        by Rachel
    The first true mammals
lived in the Late Triassic.
They were furry rat-like
animals.

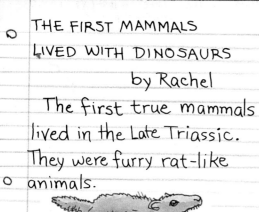

WHAT ARE MAMMALS?
            by Wanda
  Mammals are animals that:
  - have backbones
  - have hair or fur
  - are warm-blooded

  - feed their babies with
    mothers' milk

The last things we saw before we took off
were some small, furry animals.
Ms. Frizzle said they were the first mammals.
The hand on the clock moved ahead,
and the Triassic rain forest whizzed out of sight.

Ring! Ring! The alarm went off,
and we heard Ms. Frizzle say, "Oh no!"
We had stopped too soon.
It was the Late Jurassic Period,
the Age of Giants!

WHAT WAS THE EARTH LIKE THEN?

Continents were drifting apart.
• Swampy, low-lying plains
• Beginnings of inland seas
• Beginning of Atlantic Ocean
• Warm temperatures everywhere

APATOSAURUS
(ALSO CALLED BRONTOSAURUS)

HERE ARE SOME INTERESTING TREE TRUNKS.

UM... I DON'T THINK SO.

WHERE WE ARE IN TIME

PRESENT TIME

CENOZOIC ERA
65 MILLION YEARS AGO

CRETACEOUS
144 MILLION YEARS AGO

JURASSIC
213 MILLION YEARS AGO

LATE TRIASSIC
225 MILLION YEARS AGO

23

WHAT WERE SAUROPODS?
by Amanda Jane

Sauropods were heavy, long-necked dinosaurs. They walked on four legs and ate plants.

SOME KINDS OF SAUROPODS

ULTRASAURUS

BRACHIOSAURUS

DIPLODOCUS

APATOSAURUS

SEISMOSAURUS

"Notice these sauropod dinosaurs, children," said Ms. Frizzle.
They were kind of impossible to miss.
They were the largest land animals that ever lived!

STONES IN STOMACH GRIND UP FOOD

SIXTY MILLION YEARS HAVE PASSED SINCE WE WERE HERE LAST.

LOOK! THOSE SAUROPODS ARE SWALLOWING THEIR FOOD WHOLE!

THEIR TEETH ARE NOT GOOD FOR CHEWING, PHOEBE.

THEY SWALLOW STONES TO GRIND U[P] FOOD IN THEIR STOMACHS.

Sauropods!

NOW

THEN

LATER

WE KNOW DINOSAURS LAID EGGS

by Amanda Jane

Fossil dinosaur eggs have been found. Inside some, there are tiny skeletons of babies.

HOW BIG WERE DINOSAUR EGGS?

by Molly

The largest dinosaur egg we have found was about the size of a football!

Under a pile of leaves, we found some dinosaur eggs just about to hatch!
Nearby some stegosaurs — plated dinosaurs — were eating plants.
One of the stegosaurs had a hurt leg.

26

Suddenly an *Allosaurus* approached the wounded *Stegosaurus*. *Stegosaurus*'s spiked tail lashed out. It missed *Allosaurus* by an inch! What would happen next? We held our breath.

serrated edge

ALLOSAURUS TOOTH (actual size)

IT'S HARD TO BE A HUNTER
by Alex
Being a predator is dangerous. Predators can get hurt or killed by their prey. This is why meat-eaters often attack prey that is weak, sick, or young.

Allosaurus darted close and took a big bite.
Then it moved back and waited.
Stegosaurus got weaker and weaker.
It had become food for Allosaurus.

CLASS, WHATEVER ALLOSAURUS DOES NOT EAT WILL FEED OTHER DINOSAURS, TOO.

AT MY OLD SCHOOL WE NEVER GOT THIS CLOSE TO PREDATORS.

I GUESS THAT STEGOSAURUS WON'T BECOME A DINOSAUR FOSSIL.

NO. IT'S BECOMING A DINOSAUR DINNER.

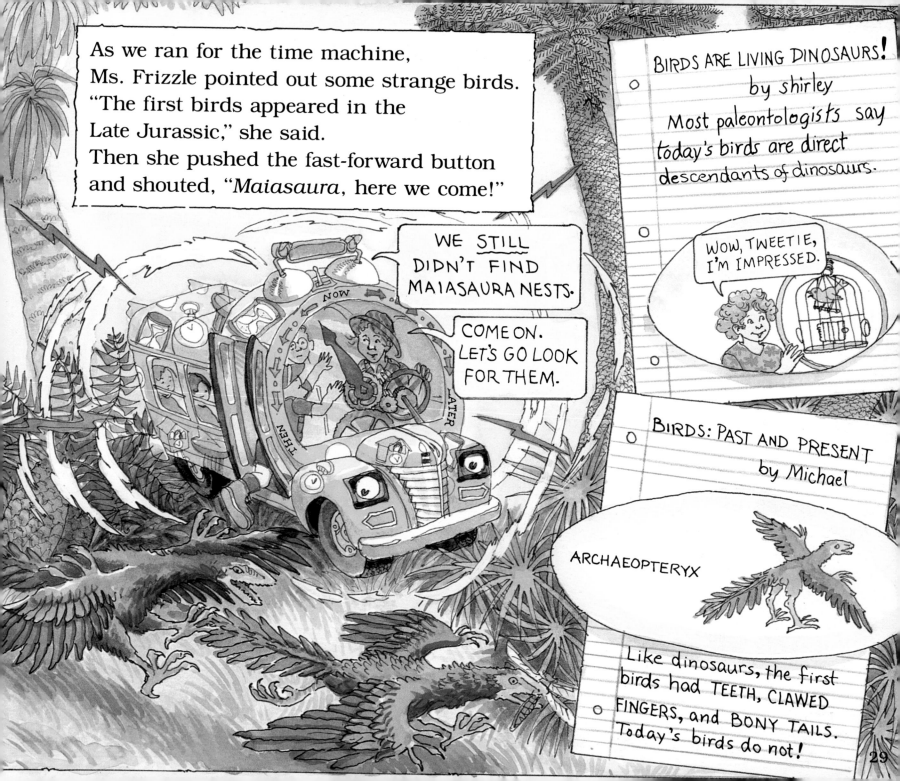

As we ran for the time machine,
Ms. Frizzle pointed out some strange birds.
"The first birds appeared in the
Late Jurassic," she said.
Then she pushed the fast-forward button
and shouted, "*Maiasaura*, here we come!"

WE STILL DIDN'T FIND MAIASAURA NESTS.

COME ON. LET'S GO LOOK FOR THEM.

BIRDS ARE LIVING DINOSAURS!
by shirley
Most paleontologists say today's birds are direct descendants of dinosaurs.

WOW, TWEETIE, I'M IMPRESSED.

BIRDS: PAST AND PRESENT
by Michael

ARCHAEOPTERYX

Like dinosaurs, the first birds had TEETH, CLAWED FINGERS, and BONY TAILS. Today's birds do not!

29

ALL DINOSAURS WERE LAND ANIMALS
by Gregory

No dinosaurs lived in the sea. During the Cretaceous, dinosaurs lived in places that were not covered by water.

WE WON'T SEE ANY DINOSAURS HERE.

Ring! Ring! The alarm went off again.
We looked out — and then we freaked out!
Once again, we had stopped too soon.
"Here we are in the Late Cretaceous Period,"
announced Ms. Frizzle.
"At this time there was a sea
right in the middle of our continent."

WE'RE IN THE SAME PLACE 25 MILLION YEARS LATER.

HOW TIME FLIES.

THAT'S NOT ALL THAT FLIES.

PTERANODON

PRESENT TIME

CENOZOIC ERA 65 MILLION YEARS AGO

CRETACEOUS 144 MILLION YEARS AGO

JURASSIC 213 MILLION YEARS AGO

LATE TRIASSIC 225 MILLION YEARS AGO

WHERE WE ARE IN TIME

Out the windows, enormous sea reptiles swam by.
Overhead, flying reptiles glided past,
dipping their beaks in the water to catch fish.
We were getting a little wet,
so the Friz set the clock ahead again.

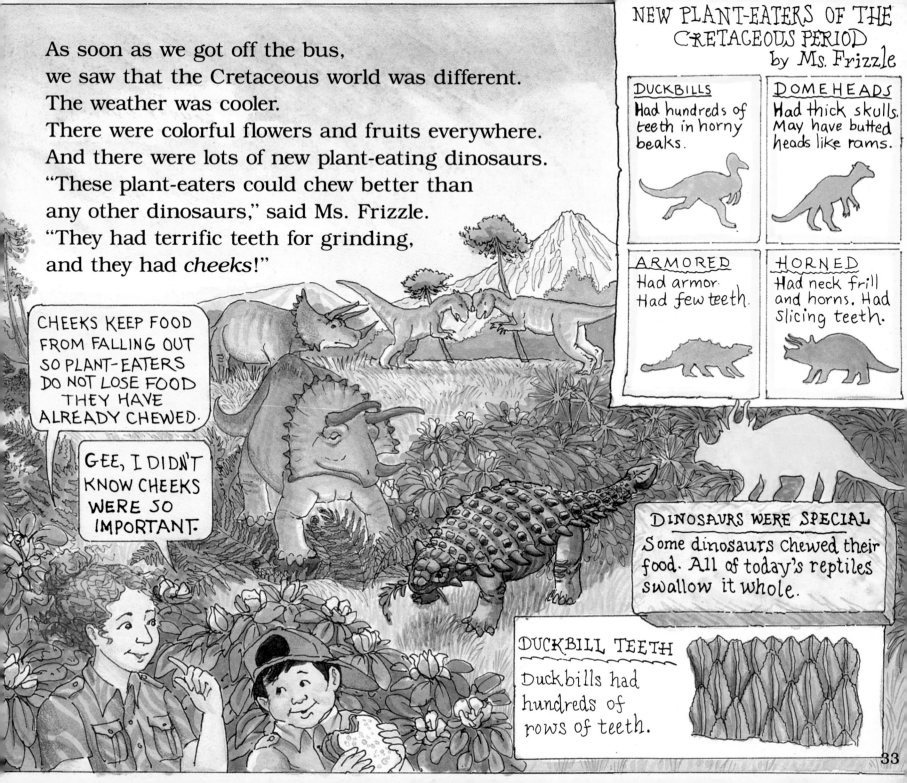

As soon as we got off the bus,
we saw that the Cretaceous world was different.
The weather was cooler.
There were colorful flowers and fruits everywhere.
And there were lots of new plant-eating dinosaurs.
"These plant-eaters could chew better than
any other dinosaurs," said Ms. Frizzle.
"They had terrific teeth for grinding,
and they had *cheeks*!"

CHEEKS KEEP FOOD FROM FALLING OUT SO PLANT-EATERS DO NOT LOSE FOOD THEY HAVE ALREADY CHEWED.

GEE, I DIDN'T KNOW CHEEKS WERE SO IMPORTANT.

NEW PLANT-EATERS OF THE CRETACEOUS PERIOD
by Ms. Frizzle

DUCKBILLS
Had hundreds of teeth in horny beaks.

DOMEHEADS
Had thick skulls. May have butted heads like rams.

ARMORED
Had armor. Had few teeth.

HORNED
Had neck frill and horns. Had slicing teeth.

DINOSAURS WERE SPECIAL
Some dinosaurs chewed their food. All of today's reptiles swallow it whole.

DUCKBILL TEETH
Duckbills had hundreds of rows of teeth.

33

The tyrannosaurs were scary enough.
Then a pack of *Troodon* showed up, too!
They were small, but there were a lot of them!
They began circling the bus to see what it was.
We sized up the situation and ran.

As we came over the crest of a hill,
we saw an incredible sight!
It was the *Maiasaura* nesting ground!

WHY DO WE THINK MAIASAURA BABIES GREW UP IN NESTS?

by Wanda

When scientists found the first Maiasaura nests, they saw:

- Crushed eggshells, showing that babies might have stayed in nests and stepped on shells.
- Skeletons of different sizes, showing that babies might have grown bigger in nests.

- Worn down baby teeth, showing that babies might have eaten food brought by parents.

37

We weren't the only ones
who had found the *Maiasaura*.
The *Troodon* had followed us.
They invaded the nesting ground.
The *Maiasaura* parents defended their young.
All at once, a sandstorm blew up.
In minutes, a thick layer of sand
covered the dinosaurs.

Everything happened so fast.
There was no way we could help
the dinosaurs.
Maybe they would become fossils.

OH, NO!
I DROPPED
MY MODEL
MAIASAURA!

HURRY UP
AND RUN!

Back in the bus, Ms. Frizzle drove
forward in time.
We thought we were going home,
but, on the way,
the bus screeched to a stop.

STRUTHIOMIMUS

PRESENT TIME

CENOZOIC ERA
65 MILLION YEARS AGO

CRETACEOUS
144 MILLION YEARS AGO

JURASSIC
213 MILLION YEARS AGO

LATE TRIASSIC
225 MILLION YEARS AGO

WHERE WE ARE IN TIME

39

"We are in the very last minutes of the Cretaceous Period," said Ms. Frizzle. A bright light was shining in the sky. "Notice that asteroid," said the Friz. "It's a huge rock from outer space. Soon it will hit the earth."

THE ASTEROID WILL CAUSE AN ENORMOUS EXPLOSION... BLACK SOOT WILL FILL THE AIR AND BLOCK OUT THE SUN... PLANTS WON'T GROW, AND MILLIONS OF LIVING THINGS WILL BECOME EXTINCT — INCLUDING THE DINOSAURS.

MS. FRIZZLE, COULD WE LEAVE BEFORE THE ASTEROID HITS?

LAMBEOSAURUS

40

The Friz pushed the forward button, and we started again.

WE'RE ONLY 65 MILLION YEARS FROM HOME, CLASS.

STEP ON IT, PLEASE...

When the alarm rang, we were back in our own time.
The paleontologists were worried about us,
and came looking for us.
We gave them a tip on a fossil site.
Then we waved good-bye and drove back to school.

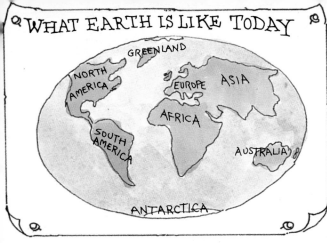

In the classroom, we made a chart
of our trip to the dinosaurs.
Just as we were finishing it,
people started coming in for Visitors Day.

The visitors admired everything.
They had never seen such fabulous projects,
such wonderful books, or such an incredible video.
And, of course, they had never met a teacher
quite like Ms. Frizzle!

YOUR BONES ARE THE BEST, HONEY.

THANKS, GRAN.

HEY, LOOK AT THOSE SPECIAL EFFECTS!

THE DINOSAURS SEEM SO REAL!

VCR TAPE PLAYER

WHY FLORRIE, THIS READS AS IF YOU WERE REALLY THERE.

IT OUGHT TO.

MODEL OF DINOSAUR SKELETON by Phoebe. Made from chicken bones and clay

THE DAY I MET A MAIASAURA by Florrie

44

45

FROM THE AUTHOR'S DESK...

DINOSAURS
Dinosaurs
dinosaurs
Dinosaurs
and for a change...
MORE DINOSAURS

Joanna Cole

Birds are the dinosaurs of today.
- They live in groups.
- They feed their babies.
- They are warm-blooded.

A BUS CAN'T BECOME A TIME MACHINE —THERE'S NO SUCH THING!

KIDS CAN'T GO BACK IN TIME!

YOUR TEACHER WAS NOT AROUND IN THE TIME OF THE DINOSAURS.

Dear Valerie— As you can see, we found the fossil Maiasaura nests. Thanks! Jeff

P.S. I wonder how we could have found a plastic Maiasaura model buried in a fossil nest!?

DEAR JEFF, HERE ARE SOME LETTERS FROM MY CLASS — Valerie

I ♡ dinosaurs too. —Tim

We hope you like our video. —John

I want to be a paleontologist too! —Keesha

Did Ms. Frizzle dress that way in high school? MOLLY & AMANDA JANE

WATER WORKS
OCEAN FLOOR
SOLAR SYSTEM
HUMAN BODY
EARTH

OLD RESEARCH FILES

MUFFY